2023. 2 권선율

갯마을 차차차 포토에세이 출간을 축하드립니다.

갯마을 차차차 포토에세이

1

갯마을 차차차

포토에세이 1

초판 1쇄 발행 2023년 2월 14일
초판 2쇄 발행 2023년 3월 14일

제작 | 스튜디오드래곤

펴낸이 | 金滇珉
펴낸곳 | 북로그컴퍼니
책임편집 | 김나정
디자인 | 김승은

사진 | [STILL ALIVE]한성경
포스터 사진 | 강현인
번역 | 정진서(Jinsuh Jung-Aum)

주소 | 서울시 마포구 와우산로 44(상수동), 3층
전화 | 02-738-0214
팩스 | 02-738-1030
등록 | 제2010-000174호

ISBN 979-11-6803-044-2   04810
      979-11-6803-043-5   04810 (세트)

우리의 마음이 춤추기 시작한 순간

포토에세이

....

1

갯마을 차차차

북로그컴퍼니

Contents

Synopsis ⸻ 6

Cast ⸻ 8

1 당신의 모습을, 어디서나 만난 순간
The moment I first met you ⸻ 18

2 당신의 진심이, 한 발짝 나아간 순간
The moment you took a step forward ⸻ 54

3 당신의 마음이, 내게 미소 지은 순간
The moment you smiled at me ⸻ 92

4 당신의 온도가, 나의 마음을 녹인 순간
The moment your temperature melted my heart ⸻ 160

5   당신의 감정이, 파도에 떠오른 순간

The moment your emotions rose over the waves   ······ 210

6   당신의 시선이, 우정을 넘어선 순간

The moment you wanted to be more-than-friends   ······ 288

7   당신의 외로움이, 나에게 기대온 순간

The moment you leaned on me   ······ 336

8   당신의 존재가, 어둠을 지우는 순간

The moment your existence erases the darkness   ······ 404

Synopsis

이 이야기는 청호시 공진동에서 벌어지는 활기차고 리드미컬한 갯마을 스토리다. 대문은 없고 오지랖은 쩔고 의좋은 형제처럼 음식 봉다리가 오가는 이곳에서 평균체온이 1도쯤 높을 게 분명한, 뜨끈한 인간들의 '만유人력'이 작동한다!

삶의 템포가 정반대인 두 남녀가 신나게 서로의 발을 밟아대는 불협화음 러브스토리다. 성취지향형 여자 '윤혜진'과 행복추구형 남자 '홍반장'의 호흡은 그야말로 최악. 리듬은 놓치고 박자는 틀리고 엉망진창인데, 그게 어쩐지 재미있어지기 시작한다. 밀고 당기다 꼬이고 엉켜버린 이들의 티키타카 로맨스가 4분의 4박자로 펼쳐진다!

매 순간 모두가 주인공이 될 수 있는 휴먼스토리다. 모든 존재는 저마다의 가치가 있다는 것을, 때론 진주보다 햇볕에 반짝이는 모래알이 더 빛이 난다는 것을 보여주는 평범한 사람들의 위대하고도 특별한 일상이 밀려온다!

This rom-com slice-of-life drama takes place in the vibrant and lively seaside town of Gongjin. Here, everyone keeps their gates unlocked, shares their home-cooked food, and takes care of each other like one big family. These countryside people are so warmhearted that their body temperatures are probably 1 degree Celsius higher than the average!

Our two protagonists include achievement-oriented Yoon Hye-jin and free-spirited Chief Hong. Although Hye-jin and Chief Hong could not be any more different, their rocky first meeting gradually evolves into a beautiful romance.

As we are led through the personal lives and stories of the other townsfolk, we are reminded that everyone is the main character in their own lives. The stories of Hye-jin, Chief Hong, and the humble townspeople foster a fondness and an appreciation for the daily lives of ordinary people.

윤혜진 YOON HYE-JIN

신민아 ——— Shin Min-a

사랑스러움의 의인화 그 자체다. 그런데 직업까지 치과의사다. 현재는 페이닥터로 억대 연봉을 받고 있다. 이렇게 완벽해 보이는 그녀의 실체는 사실... 모순덩어리다! 교과서 위주로 공부하고 전공만 판 덕분일까. 일반상식이 부족하다. 사회적 약자를 위한 정기후원을 하고 있지만, 개인주의자에 쇼핑 중독자다. 공주님처럼 보이지만 실은 자수성가의 아이콘이다. 어려서부터 집안이 어려웠고, 대학등록금과 생활비가 버거워 매일을 시간에 쫓기듯 살았다. 그렇게 힘들게 의사가 되었으니 이제는 돈과 성공으로 보상받아야 할 차례라고 생각한다. 몇 년 후 서울에 자신의 병원을 개원할 계획이었지만 과잉진료를 강요하는 원장을 들이받은 후로 모든 계획이 틀어져버린다. 우여곡절 끝에 공진에 내려가게 된 혜진은, 그곳에서 치과를 개원하려다 정체불명의 남자 '홍반장'을 만난다. 멀쩡하게 생겨서는 동네 잡다구리한 일이나 맡아 하는 반백수! 자꾸만 온갖 일에 참견하고 오지랖을 부리는 남자. 여러 소문을 몰고 다니는 이 미스터리한 남자가 너무너무 거슬리다가... 궁금해지기 시작한다.

Hye-jin is an independent and individualistic young woman with a charming appearance and a shopping addiction. At first glance, her designer shoes and jewelry give off the impression that she is a spoiled princess, but she is actually self-made! Throughout college, she worked tirelessly day in and day out to pay for her college tuition and living expenses because of her family's difficult financial situation. After years of hard work, she became a well-paid dentist. However, due to various obstacles to opening her own dental clinic in Seoul, she eventually moves to a small seaside town called Gongjin. There, she meets a handsome but strange man people call "Chief Hong." Hye-jin keeps finding Chief Hong at the center of all town activities and begins to get more curious about him.

홍두식 HONG DU-SIK

김선호 ___ Kim Seon-ho

그 남자의 이목구비에는 서사庶事가 있다. 완벽한 하드웨어에 판타스틱한 소프트웨어까지 갖춘 이 남자를 사람들은 '홍반장'이라 부른다. 두식은 몇 년째 공진동 5통 1반의 반장으로 활동 중이다. 봉사라 봐도 무방한 명예직! 그렇다. 이 남자의 공식적인 직업은... 무직이다. 직업은 없지만 하는 일은 무한대에 가깝다. 각종 아르바이트로 생계를 유지하며 페이는 딱 최저시급 8,720원만 받는다. 두식이 이렇게 사는 이유가 다들 궁금하지만, 답을 아는 이는 없다. 두식의 5년간의 공백에 대한 추측도 난무하는데, 그는 한 번도 입을 연 적이 없다. 확실한 건 5년이 그의 인생을 바꿔놨다는 사실이다. 자연스럽게 흘러가는 대로 놔두는 것, 그 후로 두식이 선택한 삶의 방식이다. 그는 타고난 오지랖으로 이웃의 모든 대소사에 관여한다. 다정하거나 살뜰하진 못해도 투박하게 따뜻하다. 이런 두식 앞에 그와는 전혀 다른 여자 혜진이 나타난다. 사람들을 향해 금을 딱 그어놓고 깍쟁이같이 구는 여자. 그런 주제에 쓸데없이 성실하고 열정적인 여자. 이 여자가 자꾸만 두식의 신경을 건드리기 시작한다.

Du-sik has been Gongjin's chief for the past few years. More commonly referred to as "Chief Hong," he appears wherever and whenever someone needs help. While he is technically unemployed, he has many responsibilities throughout the town and makes a living by doing various tasks for only minimum-wage. It is unclear why he chose this sort of lifestyle. Rumors are rampant about his recent five-year absence from Gongjin, but he's never spoken about it. The only thing that is apparent is that those five years dramatically affected him in some way. Suddenly, he meets a young woman who is his polar opposite: Yoon Hye-jin. His first impression of her is that she has a cold and individualistic personality. As he keeps running into her, he finds that she gets on his nerves and doesn't know what to do with her.

지성현 JI SEONG-HYEON

이상이 _____ Lee Sang-yi

    요즘 방송계에서 '지성현'을 모르면 간첩이다. ovN의 예능 PD로 따뜻한 관찰예능, 친인간적 콘텐츠로 공전의 히트를 기록하고 있다. 어릴 땐 영화감독을, 커서는 기자를 지망했으나, 엉뚱하게도 예능 PD가 되었다. 인생은 항상 자신을 더 재미있는 쪽으로 데려간다는 믿음이 있다. 직장 동료들을 친구로, 아이디어 회의를 수다로 생각하는 해맑은 워커홀릭이지만, 사람들은 모두 성현을 좋아한다. 마음에 꼬인 구석 없이, 어떤 의견이라도 수용할 줄 아는 사람이다. 그런 그가 유일하게 고집을 피우는 분야는 바로 음식! 굶으면 예민해지고, 맛없는 걸로 배 채우는 건 혐오한다. 성현이 혜진을 만난 건 대학 시절 한 교양수업에서였다. 시간에 치여 바빠 살면서도 항상 눈이 초롱초롱하던 혜진이 기특하고 예뻤다. 그런 그녀를 언젠가 꼭 한 번 다시 만나고 싶다 생각했다. 그런데 그게 여기일 줄은 몰랐다. 새로운 예능 프로그램 촬영지를 답사하던 중 길을 잘못 들어 발견한 공진항! 성현은 생각한다. 운명이 자신을 여기로 데려다놓은 게 아닐까 하고.

    Seong-hyeon is a well-known producer: best known for his warm and relatable TV shows. He has a go-with-the-flow personality and trusts that his life will lead him to do fun things. Even though he's a workaholic who views his co-workers as friends and his content meetings as a place for friendly chit-chat, he is well-liked by everyone. The only thing he is picky about is his food. He becomes sensitive when he is hungry and hates filling his stomach with bad food. Seong-hyeon first met Hye-jin in an elective class during his college years. He thought she was really pretty and admired her strong work ethic. Even after graduating, he never forgot about her. One day, Seong-hyeon takes a wrong turn into Gongjin while location-hunting for his next TV show and coincidentally runs into Hye-jin! Having met his first love again, he believes that fate has brought him to this town.

1

당신의 모습을, 어디서나 만난 순간
The moment I first met you

서울 대형 치과에서 일하는 치과의사 혜진은 어느 날 환자에게 눈탱이나 씌우는 원장을 확 들이받는다. 그간 수고한 자신에게 값비싼 구두를 셀프 하사하고, 루프탑 와인 바에서 신나게 퇴사 자축 파티까지. 여기 아니면 내가 뭐 갈 데 없을 줄 알고? 하지만 쓰는 이력서마다 번번이 떨어지고, 채용 연락인가 싶어 들여다본 휴대폰 알림에는 카드 값 약 700만 원이 찍혀 있다. 그리고 그 옆의 또 다른 알림, '엄마 생일'.

혜진이 7살이던 때 가족 여행으로 떠났던 공진 바다. 잘나가던 인생이 하루아침에 고꾸라진 혜진은 공진을 찾고, 공진은 혜진에게 자꾸 방해물을 얹는다. 구두 한 짝은 파도에 휩쓸려가고, 화장실이 급해 들어간 카페에서는 카드가 긁히지 않는다. 휴대폰도, ATM도 다 먹통. '뭐 이런 동네가 있나?' 싶은데 한국통신 청호지사에 불이 났단다. 난감해진 혜진의 눈앞에 나타난 건 바로 떠내려간 구두 한 짝을 건져줬던 서핑남. 커피 값을 빌려 달라 하자 "빌려주는 대신 벌게 해줄게."라고 답하는 그를 따라 혜진은 난생처음 할복장에서 오징어 배를 가르고 내장을 뜯는다.

예상치 못한 하루를 보낸 혜진은 서울로 돌아가다가 원장에게 걸려온 전화를 받는다. "치과의사 커뮤니티에 실명 까고 원장 욕한 내부고발자를 누가 돈을 주고 쓰겠어?" 그 말에 확 돌아버린 혜진. 까짓것, 부동산 값 싸고 치과 없는 공진에 내가 개원하면 되지! 그렇게 다시 도착한 공진에서 부동산 공인중개사를 소개받는데 어제 봤던 그 남자다. 홍반장, 홍두식!

Yoon Hye-jin, who has been working in a dental clinic in Seoul, confronts her Dental Clinic Manager about how she keeps pushing Hye-jin to encourage expensive and unnecessary treatments to the clients. The argument concludes with her quitting her job. After leaving, she purchases expensive shoes and treats herself to a work-leaving party at a nice rooftop wine bar. "It's not like I can't work somewhere else if I quit here" she thinks. However, with each resume she sends, she receives a rejection email in return. Her phone dings and she excitedly looks down in hopes that it's about a job, but it's a notice that her card has a remaining balance of 7 million won (approx. $6000 USD). The notification next to it reads "Mom's Birthday."

When Hye-jin was 7 years old, she went on a family trip to a town called Gongjin. With her once-stable life starting to fall apart, she makes the bold decision to visit Gongjin. Once arriving, however, she faces a series of obstacles. First, her shoe is swept away by the waves. Then, her card gets declined in a cafe she visits to use the bathroom and neither her mobile card or the nearby ATM work. As she starts to wonder whether there is something wrong with this town, she hears that the Chungho branch of the Telecom company caught on fire, which explains why her mobile card didn't work. Still, this revelation did not help the fact that she was 4,000 won short. Suddenly, the surfer man who rescued her missing shoe earlier catches her eye, and she asks him if he can lend her 4,000 won for her coffee. He replies "Instead of having you borrow it, I'll help you earn it," and as a result, Hye-jin learns to remove squid innards for the first time in her life.

After spending a crazy day in Gongjin, she starts to head back to Seoul. She receives a call from the Dental Clinic Manager saying that she's been blacklisted by the dentist community in Seoul for her rebellious behavior against her manager. Hearing this, she decides to open a dental clinic in Gongjin, where there's no dentists and real estate is cheap. After arriving in Gongjin again, she looks for the real estate agent and finds that he is the same man who helped her yesterday: Du-sik.

그래가지고 병원 문 박차고 나가자마자,
백화점에 가서 신발을 샀어?

So that's why you bought luxury shoes right after you quit?

그럼! 소신껏 셀프 퇴직 선물을 하사했어.
앞으로 꽃길만 걸으라는 함축적인 메시지를 담아봤지.

Of course! It's a small retirement gift to myself.
It means that I will only walk on the "flower road*" in the future.

* flower road: In Korea, "walking on a flower road" is a saying that wishes people only happiness and success in
the future.

오늘 제가 처음 신은 구두거든요. 되게 비싼 건데.
저기, 기왕 도와주신 김에 나머지 한 짝 좀 찾아주시면 안 될까요?

Today was my first time wearing these shoes.

They were really expensive.

Since you already found this, could you help me find the other one?

4,000원. 빌리는 대신 벌게 해줄게.

돈을 어디서 어떻게 벌어요?
저 혹시 이상한 데 끌고 가는 건 아니죠?

The 4,000 won. Instead of having you borrow it, I'll help you earn it.

Where and how will I earn the money?
You're not taking me somewhere sketchy, right?

전화 안 돼서 놀랐지?

지금 전화국에 불났대.

좀만 기다리시면은 멀쩡해질 거야.

Grandma, you were surprised because your phone didn't work, right?

There's a fire at the telecom company right now.

But it should be fixed soon.

지금 나더러 오징어 내장을 따라고요?

돈 필요하다며.
안 벌 거야?

You want me to remove squid innards?

You said you needed money.
You're not going to work?

고생해서 돈 벌어보니까 어때? 애틋하지?

How does it feel to make hard-earned money? Feels good, right?

저 바다가 얼마나 이뻐.
난 공진항이 꼭 돌아가신 엄마 품 같아.

Isn't the ocean beautiful?

Gongjin Harbor has always felt like my late mother's embrace.

뭐 하는 사람이야?
대체 그쪽 정체가 뭐냐고.

What's your real job?
Who in the world are you?

나? 홍반장!

Me? I'm Chief Hong!

2

당신의 진심이, 한 발짝 나아간 순간
The moment you took a step forward

　　혜진은 불같은 추진력으로 공진에 치과를 개원한다. 부동산 임대차계약서를 시작으로 도배, 미장 등 인테리어까지 온통 두식이 맡는데 어떤 일이든 시급 8,720원만 받는단다. 처음에야 미심쩍었지만 결과를 보니 제법인 이 남자. 한편, 혜진은 통장인 화정을 통해 경로잔치에 초대받는다. 가고 싶은 마음은 없지만 치과 홍보에 도움이 될 거란 말에 혹해버렸다. 그렇게 경로잔치에 오긴 했는데 뭐 하나 마음에 드는 게 있어야지. 혜진은 주는 음식 안 먹고, 주는 마음 '턱' 쳐내기 바쁘다. 어차피 상관없지 않을까. 혜진에게 공진은 돈만 바짝 벌어 금방 떠날 곳이니까. 시끄러운 마당을 벗어나 마을회관 안에서 친구 미선과 통화하던 혜진은 "다 맘에 안 들어!"를 시작으로 반짝 스타였던 과거를 지겹게 우려먹는 카페 사장 춘재를 욕한다. 그런데 아뿔싸, 켜져 있던 확성기로 동네 사람들이 통화 내용을 다 들어버렸다.

　　치위생사인 미선까지 합류해 '윤치과'를 개원한 첫 날, 공진에서 미운 털 제대로 박힌 혜진을 찾는 환자는 단 한 명도 없다. 낙담한 혜진을 찾은 두식은 개업 떡을 돌려라, 반상회에 얼굴을 비춰라, 갖은 오지랖을 부리고, 딱히 방법이 없던 혜진은 두식의 말에 따라 동네 대청소까지 참여한다. 아직은 잘 섞이지 않는 공진과 혜진이지만, 시간이 지나며 치과에도 하나둘 환자들이 모여들고 활기는 띠는데…

Hye-jin starts working on her new clinic with fiery motivation. After helping her set up the real estate lease contract, Du-sik takes charge of all the interior decorations. No matter what work he does, he only requests a minimum wage. Because of this, Hye-jin is a little suspicious at first, but her suspicions are soon put to rest after seeing the quality of his work. Meanwhile, Hye-jin gets invited to the town's senior citizens party. Even though she wasn't interested, she goes to the party, thinking it will be good advertisement for her new clinic. She does not have fun at the party; she rejects the food that people offer to her and is busy keeping her distance from people. After all, what does it matter what these people think of her when she's just here to make money and leave? Hye-jin leaves the noisy yard and goes inside the community center to call her friend, Mi-seon. She complains to Mi-seon about how Chun-jae keeps talking about his boring past and about how much she hates everything about Gongjin, but the mike is still on so all of the townspeople overheard her phone call on the loudspeaker.

On the first day of opening "Yoon Dental Clinic" with her best friend and hygienist, Mi-seon, no one shows up. Du-sik offers some advice to the upset dentist and tells her to gift the townspeople rice cakes for the clinic's grand opening and recommends that she participate in the town-hall meetings. Because she is desperate, Hye-jin takes his advice and even ends up participating in a neighborhood cleaning event. As time goes by, more and more patients visit the new clinic, and the clinic starts to become more lively...

현관 비밀번호는 870724.

근데 이게 무슨 숫자야?

내 생일.

왜 남의 집 비번을 자기 생일로 해놔?
서른다섯이야? 나보다 한 살 오빠네.

오빠라 그랬어 지금? 오빠라고 부르면 죽는다.

The password to the front door is 870724.

Where's this number from?

My birthday.

Why would you set someone else's password to your birthday?
You're 35? That makes you my oppa* by 1 year.

Did you just call me oppa?
If you call me oppa again, you're dead.

* oppa: In Korea, women call men who are older than them "oppa,"
  but it is also commonly used as a term of endearment to refer to
  their boyfriend.

다 맘에 안 들어. 서울에 있을걸 괜히 왔어.
무슨 카페 하는 아저씨가 하나 있는데, 무명가수인가 봐.
매니저가 돈 들고튀는 바람에 2집을 못 냈다나?
실력이든 의지든 뭐라도 있었으면 어떻게든 잘됐겠지.
현재가 이 모양인데 과거 타령하며 사는 거, 너무 비겁하고 초라해 보여.

I hate everything here. Maybe I should've stayed in Seoul.

There's this man who runs a café here, but apparently he's also an obscure singer.

He said he couldn't finish his second album because his manager ran off with his money.

He would've made it big if he had ambition or talent.

I think it's cowardly to live in the past when your reality's a mess.

인간아, 마이크 켜놓으면 어떡해!
얼른 가서 꺼!

How could you leave the mike on?
Hurry and go turn it off!

그쪽은 본인이 잘났다고 생각하지?
머리 좋아 공부도 잘했을 테고 의사도 됐고.
인생이 아주 탄탄대로였겠어.
아, 물론 시련도 있었겠지.
어쩌다가 덜컹하는 방지턱 같은 거.
고작 그거 넘으며 역시 의지만 있으면 안 되는 게 없어, 그랬을 테고?

You think you're better than everyone.
You're smart, you were good at studying,
and you became a dentist.
You must've had such a smooth-sailing life.
Not always, of course. You probably had a few trials.
But only small speed bumps.
And after overcoming those simple speed bumps,
you thought that willpower alone could get you anywhere.

뭘 잘 모르시나 본데
인생이라는 거 그렇게 공평하지가 않아.
평생이 울퉁불퉁 비포장도로인 사람도 있고,
죽어라 달렸는데
그 끝이 낭떠러지인 사람도 있어.

I think you're misunderstanding something here.
Life isn't fair to all of us.
Some people are faced with rough,
unpaved roads for their whole lives,
while some race at full speed only to find the edge of a cliff.

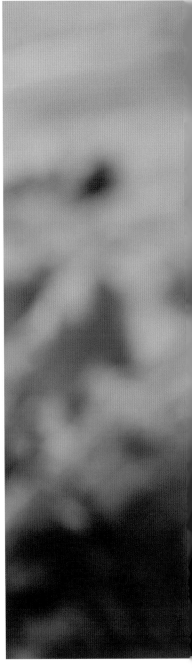

지난 후회로부터 완전히 자유로워지는 건 어쩌면 불가능하다.
살다 보면 또 다시 후회하는 일이 생길지도 모른다.
그러니 지금 우리가 할 수 있는 건 오직 하나뿐이다.
담담히 받아들이고, 앞으로 한 발짝 나아가는 것.

It's probably impossible to be completely free from our last regret.
And because it's likely that we will come across more regrets in life,
there's only one thing that we can do right now.
And that is to calmly accept things as they happen
and take the next step forward.

치과에 사람이 많아진 것 같은데
다 홍반장 덕분인 것 같아.
그때 한 말도 생각해봤는데,
뭐 그쪽이 옳다는 건 아니지만
어느 정도 일리는 있는 것 같고...

The clinic has become a lot busier thanks to you.
I thought a lot about what you said last time.
Well, I'm not saying you were right,
but you have a point...

뭐라 그러는지 안 들려!
와서 얘기해!

I can't hear anything you're saying!
Come closer!

못 올라가겠어!

I can't go up!

3

당신의 마음이, 내게 미소 지은 순간
The moment you smiled at me

대학 동기 결혼식에 참석하기 위해 서울로 향하는 혜진 앞에 나타난 할머니 3인방과 두식. 다들 서울에 볼일이 있다며 당당히 동승을 요구하고, 혜진은 모두를 태운 채 왁자지껄한 분위기 속에서 겨우 서울에 도착한다. 동기 결혼식이 끝나고 주차장으로 향하던 혜진은 엄마와 애틋하게 인사를 나누는 어느 신부의 모습을 보며 멍하니 생각에 잠기는데, 그 틈을 깨며 시야에 들어온 자, 홍반장이다. 차에 휴대폰을 두고 갔다는 그를 태워 공진으로 돌아오는 길, 티격태격하면서도 어쩐지 함께 있는 게 자연스러워지는 둘이다.

며칠 후, 두식은 임플란트가 시급한 감리를 윤치과에 데려오는데, 자신에게 큰돈을 쓰는 게 부담스러운 감리는 차라리 이를 다 뽑아버리라며 치료를 거부한다. 두식은 혜진에게 감리의 치료를 설득해줄 것을 부탁하지만, 혜진은 매몰차게 거절한다. "아픈 걸 참아? 이기적인 발상이네. 부모가 진짜 자식을 위하는 일이 뭔지 알아? 아프지 말고 오래 사는 거야!" 슬픈 눈에 담긴 혜진의 진심을, 지난날을 읽어버린 두식은 차마 혜진을 잡지 못한다. 두식에게 화는 냈지만, 그 이후로 일상 곳곳에서 두식의 말이, 감리의 아픔이 떠오르는 혜진. 차마 외면하지 못한 채 감리를 찾아가고, 감리는 치료를 받기로 마음먹는다.

혜진의 집이 정전이 된 어느 날, 두식이 어둠 속에서 혜진과 함께해주고 둘은 어둠만큼이나 깊은 대화를 나눈다. 그렇게 둘은 조금 더 가까워지는데...

As Hye-jin prepares to go to Seoul to attend her friend's wedding, Du-sik and three elderly women appear in front of her. Du-sik explains that they all need to go to Seoul and asks her to give them a ride. Hye-jin ends up carpooling the four of them and they arrive in Seoul. After the wedding ceremony, Hye-jin starts to walk towards the parking lot. On the way back, she sees a bride affectionately greeting her mother and gets lost in thought. While she is staring blankly at the pair, Du-sik suddenly appears and says that he forgot his phone in her car. The two of them drive back to Gongjin. Even though the two spend the entire ride arguing, they being together starts to feel natural.

A few days later, Du-sik brings Ms. Gam-ri to the Yoon Clinic so that she can get implants. However, after hearing how expensive it will be, Ms. Gam-ri refuses the treatment, saying that she would rather get her teeth pulled than waste money on implants. Du-sik explains to Hye-jin that Ms. Gam-ri is reluctant because doesn't want to burden her kids, and asks Hye-jin to persuade Ms. Gam-ri to change her mind. To this, Hye-jin replies "So she just endures the pain? How selfish of her. Do you know what it really means to be a good parent for your kid? It's staying healthy and living for a long time!" Seeing the sad look in Hye-jin's eyes, Du-sik does not argue back. Despite her harsh words, Hye-jin is bothered by the thought of Ms. Gam-ri putting up with the pain and decides to have a talk with her. Eventually she convinces Ms. Gam-ri to receive the treatment.

One day there is a blackout at Hye-jin's house. Du-sik stays with Hye-jin in the dark, and the two share a deep conversation and begin to get a little closer...

깜짝이야. 다른 사람인 줄?
치과 오늘 서울 간다며.

Jesus, I thought you were a different person.

I heard you're going to Seoul today.

같이 가자.
다들 서울에 볼일이 있지 뭐야.

Let's go together.

It just so happens that they all need to go to Seoul.

아니, 갑자기 이러는 경우가 어디 있어?

Hey, what are you doing all of a sudden?

여기를 오면 어떡해.
누가 보면 어쩌려고!

How could you come here?
Someone might see us.

연예인이냐?
왜 이렇게 유난을 떨어.

Are you a celebrity or something?
Stop overreacting.

그거를 또 봐요? 지겹지도 않은가.
그래서 그런 노래가 있나 봐.

You're watching that again? Aren't you tired of it?
No wonder there's this song.

텔레비전에 내가 나왔으면
정말 좋겠네 정말 좋겠네.

It'd be really great if I was on TV.

치과! 내가 환자 데려왔어!

내 안 온다 했다니!

Ms. Dentist! I brought a patient!

I told ya I don't wanna go!

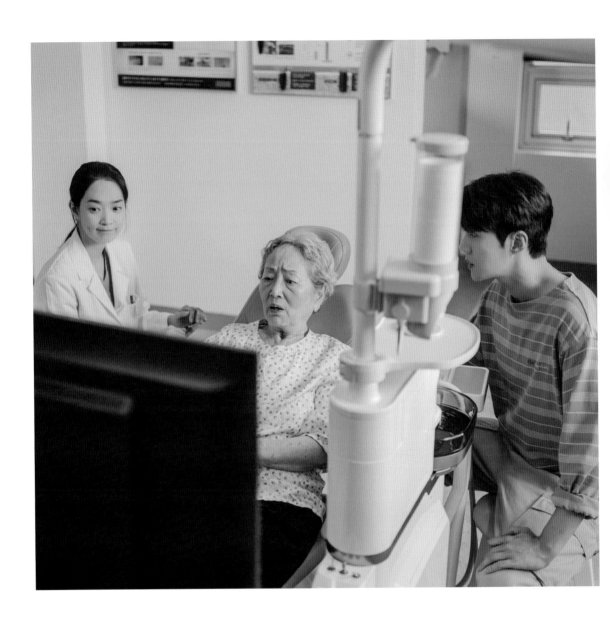

돈이 아까워서 치료를 안 하시겠다고요?
그럼 더는 드릴 말씀이 없네요. 가세요.

So you don't want to waste money on your treatment?
Well, then I have nothing left to say. Please leave.

나는 할머니가 좀 제대로 치료받았으면 좋겠어.
이 아프고 그러면 찌릿찌릿, 어우! 그거 얼마나 신경 쓰여.
그런 의미에서 내가 지금 뭘 좀 꺼낼 건데, 화내면 안 돼!
나 할머니 밥 먹고 키가 이만큼 컸잖아.
할머니 이는 내가 고쳐주고 싶어.
그러니까 이걸로 치과 가서, 우리 이 고치고 다 하자.

내 서이까지 실 테니까 니 그 안에 튀라.

Grandma, I want you to receive proper treatment.

I'm sure your toothaches are bothering you.

I'm going to take something out right now, but don't get mad!

I grew this tall because you fed me.

So as a thank you, I want to pay for your treatment.

Let's use this money to get your teeth fixed, alright?

I'll give ya three seconds to run.

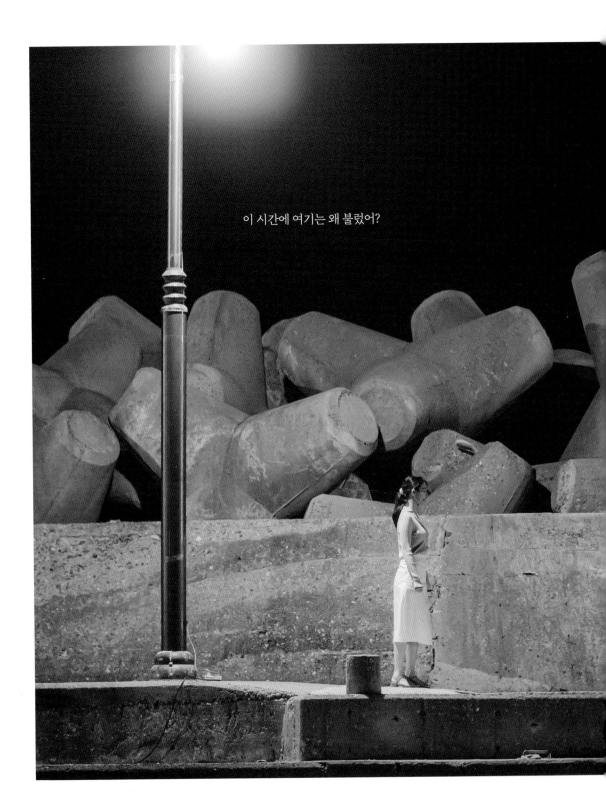

이 시간에 여기는 왜 불렀어?

Why'd you call me at this hour?

감리씨는 오징어 내장 손질만 수십 년을 했어.
근데 지겹지도 않은가 오징어를 제일로 좋아해.
못 잡순 지 한참 됐지만.
치료비는 내가 낼게. 대신 부탁이 있어.
임플란트, 비밀로 해줘.
그냥 다른 싼 치료법이라고 둘러대달라고.

그건 곤란해.
의사는 결과에 책임을 지는 사람이야.
환자에게 정확한 치료 계획을 고지할 의무가 있어.

그럼 금액이라도 다시 얘기해주라.
차액은 내가 낼 테니까,
할머니한텐 치과가 할인해주는 걸로 하고.

Ms. Gam-ri has been cleaning squids for decades.
But she never gets sick of them and loves squids the most,
even though she hasn't been able to eat them for years.
I'll pay for the treatment, but I have one favor to ask you.
Keep the implant a secret.
Just tell her it's some cheap treatment.

I can't do that.
Doctors must take responsibility for what they do.
So it's my responsibility to tell my patients what treatment they're getting.

Then tell me what the total cost will be.
I'll pay the remainder.
Just tell grandma that you gave her a discount.

대체 왜 이렇게까지 해?
본인이 안 한다잖아.

안 하는 게 아니라 못 하는 거야.
주변을 챙기는 데 인생을 바치신 분이거든.
자기를 돌보고 스스로에게 베푸는 법을 모르서.

그렇다고 아픈 걸 참아? 이기적인 발상이네.

Why are you doing this much?
She said herself that she's doesn't want it.

It's not that she doesn't want it, she can't.
She's always lived her life selflessly,
so she doesn't know how to take care of herself.

So she just endures the pain? How selfish of her.

이기적이라니! 난 할머니처럼 이타적인 사람을 본 적이 없다.
젊어서부터 자식들 위해 안 해본 일이 없고,
지금도 부담 주기 싫어서 저러시는 건데 그걸 이해 못 해?

부모가 진짜 자식을 위하는 일이 뭔지 알아?
아프지 말고 오래 사는 거야!
그깟 돈 몇 푼 물려주려고 아픈 걸 참는 게 아니라,
자기 자신부터 챙기는 거라고! 알아?

Selfish? Grandma is the most selfless person I've ever met.
Ever since she was young, she's done all kinds of work to provide for her kids.
Even now, she's acting like this because she doesn't want to burden them. Don't you get it?

Do you know what it really means to be a good parent to your kid?
It's staying healthy and living for a long time!
It's not about enduring pain to save some money for their kids.
They should take care of themselves first! Do you get it?

할머니, 근데 나 할머니한테 섭섭해.
아들이 준 용돈봉투는 넙죽넙죽 잘 받으면서
내 돈은 왜 안 받아?
나는 뭐 남이라 이거야?

Grandma, actually I'm upset with you.

You accept money from your son, but not me.

Are you saying I'm a stranger or something?

할머니. 누가 그러는데,
부모가 진짜 자식을 위하는 일은
아프지 않는 거래.

Grandma, someone told me
that the best thing a parent can do for their
child is to stay healthy.

형. 나 두식이. 잘 지내셨어?

임플란트를 해야 되는데 안 한다고 버티시네?

형님이 직접 얘기해보면 어떨까 해서.

Hyung*, it's Du-sik. How have you been?

Your mom needs implants, but she's refusing to get them.

How about you talk her through it?

* hyung: In Korean, hyung means "older brother" and is often
used by males as a friendly way to address another older male.

이 아픈 게 참 그래요.
눈에 잘 안 보이니까 자기 자신 아니면
얼마나 힘든지 잘 모르거든요.
자식들도 잘 모르고.
치과 다시 오세요.
돈을 다 안 받을 수는 없고, 재료값만 받을게요.
오징어 제일 좋아하신다면서요.
그냥 그걸 드실 수 있게 해드리고 싶어요.
그게 다예요.

Toothaches are tough.
Because they're not visible,
no one but yourself really knows how painful they are.
Not even your kids.
Please come to the clinic again.
I can't do it for free,
but I'll only charge you for the materials.
I heard your favorite food is squid.
I just want you to be able to eat squid again.
That's all.

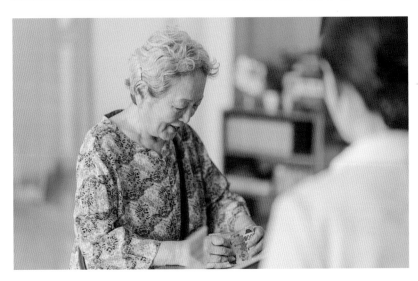

내가 잉플라르 하러 왔소.
먼첨 계산부터 해도 되오? 일시금이오.
평생을 허리껭이가 끙케 나가도록 열심히 일해왔는데.
내 죽기 전까지 오징어는 실컨 먹어야 하잖가.

I came'ta get ma implants done.
Can I pay first? Here, payment in full.
Ma whole life, I've been working my back off.
Dontcha think I deserve to eat as much squid as I want before I die?

불은 어쩌다가 나간 거야?

머리 감고 있는데 갑자기 불이 꺼졌어.

How did the blackout happen?

I was washing my hair and the lights suddenly went out.

친구는 어디 가고?
올 때까지 같이 기다려줘?

아이스크림 먹을래?
정전이 돼서 냉장고에 있는 아이스크림이 다 녹을 것 같아서.

Where's your friend?
Should I wait with you until she comes back?

Do you want to eat ice cream?
I'm just worried the ice cream will melt because of the blackout.

웬 구두가 이런 데 있어!

What's a shoe doing here!

4

당신의 온도가, 나의 마음을 녹인 순간
The moment your temperature melted my heart

　가리는 일 없이 자신이 필요한 곳이면 어디든 달려가는 홍반장이지만, 그에 앞선 제1원칙이 있었으니. 하늘이 두 쪽 나도 휴일을 지키는 것! 혜진은 온종일 보이지 않는 두식을 찾아 상가번영회에 참석하는데 사람들과 어울리는 것도, 정신을 쏙 빼놓는 시끄러운 분위기도 도무지 적응이 안 된다. 도망치기 위한 최후의 방법으로 술 취한 척 엎드린 혜진을 두식이 그대로 업고 나온다.

　윤치과에서 치료를 받던 한 환자가 미선을 성추행하고, 화가 난 혜진은 성추행범의 얼굴에 그대로 킥을 날린다. 그 순간 윤치과에 도착한 건 하늘이 두 쪽 나도 휴일은 꼭 지킨다던 홍반장! 현장에 뛰어들어 범인에게 플라잉니킥을 날려버린다. 얼마나 뛰어왔는지 기절할 듯 숨을 몰아쉬면서.

　감리와 두식의 도움으로 성추행범은 죗값을 치르고, 두식에게 고마운 마음에 혜진은 과일 바구니와 와인을 들고 두식의 집에 들렀다가 단둘이 와인을 마시게 되는데. 홍반장이 날치기범을 잡은 과거 에피소드부터 시작해 혜진이 공진에 왜 오게 됐는지 마음속 깊은 이야기를 하는 밤이고. '약해지는 게 풀어지는 게 솔직해지는 게' 싫어서 함부로 취하지 않는다던 혜진은 두식 앞에서 풀어지고, 솔직해지고, 끝내는 술에 잔뜩 취하고 만다.

Hye-jin attends the shopkeepers' meeting to advertise the dental clinic and to see Du-sik. The meeting is very loud and Hye-jin has difficulty adapting to the noisy atmosphere and socializing with the attendees. She reaches her limit and pretends to fall asleep from a hangover to escape. Du-sik leaves the meeting carrying Hye-jin on his back.

One thing to know about Du-sik is that even though he always shows up whenever and wherever he is needed without hesitation, there is one exception. And this has to do with his number one principle: to never do work on off-days. Today is one of those days. At the Yoon Dental Clinic, a client sexually assaults Mi-seon. Mi-seon does not want to make a big deal out of things and is willing to let him go, but Hye-jin decides otherwise and kicks the molester in the face. At that moment, Du-sik–the same man who swears by his number one principle of not working on his day off–rushes into the clinic and lands a flying knee kick on the molester. Du-sik has trouble breathing from how fast he ran.

Later, Hye-jin stops by Du-sik's house with wine and a fruit basket to thank him for getting the molester. The two end up drinking wine together. They exchange deep personal stories, starting from how Du-sik won two Brave Citizen Awards to the reason why Hye-jin came to Gongjin. Normally, Hye-jin doesn't get drunk because she hates feeling weak, vulnerable, and honest, but today, she was all of those things in front of Du-sik: weak, vulnerable, and honest. By the end of the night, Hye-jin is the most drunk she has been in a long time.

어이, 치과!

Hey Ms. Dentist!

어이, 치과!

Hey Ms. Dentist!

연기 그만하고 내려오시지?
안 자는 거 알아.

How about you drop the act and get down?
I know you're not sleeping.

함께 사는 세상이다.
이렇게 사람들이랑 어울리는 걸 싫어해서야...
치과, 친구도 없지?

We live in a social society.

It'll be difficult if you hate being around people...

I bet you don't have any friends.

80킬로? 미친 거 아니야?

80 kilograms? Is he crazy?

왜 이렇게 많이 줘? 배달비 2,000원이라며.

Why are you giving me this much? You said the delivery fee was 2,000 won.

됐어. 카페에 손님 없어서 잠깐 들른 거야. 간다!

It's fine. I just stopped by because there's no one at the café. I'm going now!

나 오늘은 하늘이 두 쪽 나도 일 안 해!
나한테는 휴무를 지킬 의무가 있어, 끝.

No matter what, I'm not working today!
I have a right to protect my precious holiday, end of conversation!

홍반장 니 지금 어디 있나?
여기 치과에 난리가 났다니.

Chief Hong, where are ya right now?
It's a mess at the dental clinic right now.

너 같은 성추행범은 콩밥 먹어야 해.
미선아, 경찰 불러!
미친 새끼가 진짜!

A molester like you should be in prison.

Mi-seon, call the police!

Crazy lunatic!

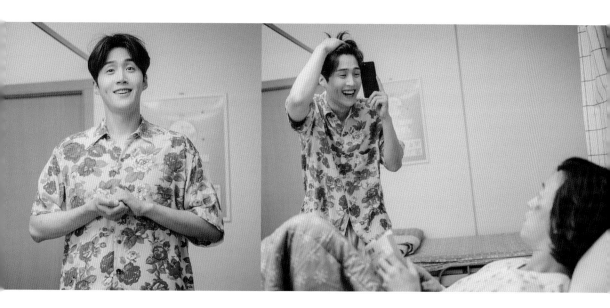

기대해. 내가 너 죗값 제대로 치르게 해줄 거니까.

너 뭔데 이렇게까지 하는 건데?
그 여자들 중에 누구랑 무슨 사이라도 되냐?

어. 되게 엄청 아주 무슨 사이야.

I'll make you pay for what you did. Look forward to it.

Who are you to be doing this much?
Do you have a relationship or something with one of those women?

Yeah, we have a huge relationship or something going on.

나 이거 사진관에서 봤었는데.
이거 홍반장이었어?

I saw this at the photo studio.

This was you?

그때 보니까 노래 좀 하더라?
내가 부탁하면 한 곡 좀 뽑아주나?

너 집에 가.

술 남았는데 어디 가.

Last time I noticed that you're quite the singer.

If I ask you to, will you sing me a song?

Go home.

I can't go home. We haven't finished the wine.

그때 보니까 경찰들이랑 친하더라.

내가 용감한 시민상을 두 번 받았거든.
한 번은 길 가다가 날치기범을 잡았고,
또 한 번은 술에 취해서 기찻길에서 잠든 할아버지를 내가 구했지.

You seemed close with the police officers.

It's because I got the Brave Citizen Award twice.
The first time was for catching a purse thief on the street,
and the second time was for saving a drunk old man sleeping on the train tracks.

공진에는 언제부터 살았어?

태어날 때부터.

한 번도 여기를 떠난 적 없어?

있지.
나한테는 선 넘지 말라 그러더니, 뭔 질문이 이렇게 많아?

나 왜 이러지? 원래 안 이러는데.
나 그쪽이 좀 신기한가 봐. 서로 환경이 너무 다르잖아.
홍반장도 나한테 딱 하나만 질문해봐.

공진에는 왜 왔어?

그날. 공진에 덜컥 왔던 날... 우리 엄마 생일이었어.
엄마 돌아가시기 전에 가족여행을 왔었어. 공진으로.

How long have you lived in Gongjin?

Since I was born.

You've never left here once?

I have.
You were the one who told me not to cross the line, but you're asking me so many questions.

What's with me today? I'm usually not like this.
I guess I just find you interesting since our lives are so different.
You can ask me one question too.

Why did you come to Gongjin?

That day. The day I came to Gongjin... was my mom's birthday.
Before my mom passed away, we went on a family trip to Gongjin.

나 진짜 미쳤나 봐.

아, 얼굴 너무 뜨거운 것 같아.

열이 좀 나는 것 같기도 하고. 나 얼굴 빨개?

뜨겁다... 너무.

I must be crazy.

My face feels so hot.

I think I might have a mild fever. Is my face red?

It's so... hot.

5

당신의 감정이, 파도에 떠오른 순간
The moment your emotions rose over the waves

술에 취해 필름이 끊긴 혜진은 괴로움에 몸부림치고, 마을에는 두 사람의 하룻밤 소문이 파다하다. 혜진은 동네 사람들이 보는 데서 두식과 아침식사를 하며 소문을 덮으려 하지만, 도리어 혜진의 입가를 닦아주는 두식. 그런 둘을 보며 "전혀 케미가 없는데? 별일 없었나 봐." 사람들은 오히려 실망하고.

혜진과 두식의 소문은 '둘 중 누가 더 아까운지', '어릴 적부터 두식이 얼마나 똑똑했는지'로 이어졌다가 두식이 공진으로 돌아오기 전 5년간의 미스터리한 행방에 대한 추측으로 옮겨간다. 간첩이었다, 국정원 비밀 요원이었다, 사람을 죽여 감옥에 다녀왔다…

두식이 자꾸만 눈과 마음에 밟히는 혜진. 참지 못하고 "홍반장, 설마 나 좋아해?"라고 물어보는데 전혀 예상하지 못한 답이 돌아온다. "짜증 나, 진짜." 민망해진 혜진은 우리는 '소셜 포지션'이 다르다며 대차게 응수하지만, 홍반장이 서울대 출신이라는 얘기에 바로 무안해지는 한편, 그런 그가 왜 지금은 반 백수로 사는지 더욱 궁금해진다.

혜진과 두식이 청진초등학교에서 구강 보건 교육을 진행한 날, 저녁을 먹고 함께 식당에서 나오려는 찰나 비가 쏟아진다. 두식은 우산을 펴려는 혜진의 손을 잡고 그대로 빗속으로 뛰어들고, 두 사람은 그렇게 비를 맞으며 신나게 뛰어논다. 그때 혜진의 머릿속에 번뜩 떠오르는 건 어젯밤 두식과 나눈 키스!

Hye-jin spends the night at Du-sik's house after getting blackout drunk. In the morning, a neighbor catches Hye-jin leaving Du-sik's house. Rumors quickly spread throughout the town that the two had spent a night together. Hye-jin tries to kill the rumors by nonchalantly eating breakfast with Du-sik while the townspeople are watching. After Du-sik wipes food off her mouth, Hye-jin thinks that her plan is ruined, but it is what actually convinces the townspeople that there is nothing going on between them. The townspeople conclude that there is no chemistry between the two of them, and leave the restaurant disappointed.

The rumors of Hye-jin and Du-sik spark a debate among the townspeople of who is better. Pointing out that Du-sik has been smart since he was a kid, some of the townspeople argue that he is too good for Hye-jin. This leads into a discussion about the mysterious whereabouts of Du-sik for the five years before he returned to Gongjin. The townspeople come up with wild theories: that he is a North Korean spy, that he is a Korean secret agent, and that he returned from prison after murdering someone.

Hye-jin can't get Du-sik out of her mind. Unable to resist, she ends up asking him if he has feelings for her and gets an unexpected answer. After hearing this, she gets very flustered and responds with a hurtful remark that they wouldn't work as a couple because their social positions are too different. Hye-jin later learns that Du-sik isn't the uneducated man she thought he was, but actually a Seoul National University alum! She immediately feels embarrassed about what she said to him and starts to get more curious about why he's unemployed.

Hye-jin and Du-sik go to an elementary school together to teach students how to brush their teeth. After finishing their lesson, the two go out to dinner together. On their way out, it is pouring rain. Before Hye-jin can finish opening up her umbrella, Du-sik grabs her hand and pulls her into the rain. The two play in the rain and get soaked. Suddenly, Hye-jin remembers that she kissed Du-sik last night!

나 김연아 같지?
우럭아~
우리 집 비밀번호는 팔... 칠... 공... 칠... 이... 사...
홍반장! 나 대빵 잘하지?

I look like Yuna Kim, right?
Rockfish~
The password is 8... 7... 0... 7... 2... 4...
Chief Hong! I'm really good at this, right?

급하게 가셨구만.

Seems like she left in a hurry.

글쎄 홍반장네 집에서 치과 윤선생이 나오는 거 있지?
이 이른 아침에 것도 도둑고양이처럼 살금살금.

Guess what? I just saw the dentist leave from Chief Hong's house.
Early in the morning, creeping away like a sneaky cat.

어이, 치과!
새벽같이 내뺐더라? 설거지도 안 하고.
해장은 했냐?

아직 출근 전인데 조찬 회동 어때?

Hey Ms. Dentist!
You left so early, without even doing the dishes.
Did you get over your hangover?

I still have time before going to work. Do you want to get breakfast?

동네에 소문 다 났어. 어젯밤 우리가... 동침했다고.
그래서 말인데... 우리 별일 없었지?

A rumor has spread all over town that we... slept together.

So uh... anyway nothing happened yesterday, right?

별일이... 엄청 많았지.
갑자기 술 먹다가 뛰어나가더니
노래하고 춤추고 철봉에 매달리더니
'나 김연아 같지?' 이러더니 또 뛰어.
막 또 뛰기 시작하면서 '두식이 오빠!'
진짜 혼자 보기 아깝더라.
거기다 뭐?
2차 가야 된다고 생떼, 난리를 쓰더니
결국엔 다시 우리 집으로 돌아와가지고
내 담금주 컬렉션 아작 내는데...

Actually... a lot happened.

While drinking you suddenly ran out

and started singing, dancing, and hanging from a pole.

You said "I look like Yuna Kim, right?" and then you ran again.

You kept running and yelling "Du-sik oppa!"

It was a waste to witness such a spectacle alone.

You know what else you did?

You made a huge fuss about going for a second round of drinking.

So we went back to my house

and you did a huge number on my homemade wine collection.

애냐? 입에 묻히고 먹게?

아니, 사람들이 더 오해하잖아!
홍반장 때문에 다 망했어.
태연하게 밥 같이 먹는 걸로 소문 무마시키려 그랬는데,
여기서 입은 왜 닦아주는 거야?
이제 또 잘 어울리네 어쩌네, 난리 나겠네 진짜!

Are you a kid? Wipe your mouth.

Wait, they'll misunderstand more!
You just ruined everything.
I was going to calm down the rumor by nonchalantly eating with you,
Ugh, now they're going to gossip more about how good we look together.

저 두 사람... 케미가 1도 없지 않아?

그지? 이게 음악으로 치면은 훅이 없어. 이게 좀 밍숭맹숭해.

보라 아빠가 보라 입 닦아줄 때랑 비슷한 느낌이에요.

어머, 어젯밤에 아무 일도 없었나 보다.

Doesn't it seem like those two have no chemistry together?

Right? If I were to compare it to music, it's as if there's no hook. It's so bland.

He wiped her mouth like how Geum-cheol wipes his daughter's.

Gosh, I guess nothing actually happened last night.

우리 홍반장이 아까워요.

다들 양심 가출하셨네.
아니, 아무리 그래도 두식이를 어디 치과의사한테 갖다 붙여요?

두식이 훌륭하지. 근데 윤선생 괜찮잖아.

중복투표 안 돼요. 혜진이에요, 아니면은 홍반장이에요?

Our Chief Hong is too good for Dr. Yoon.

You're all so shameless.
How could you say that Du-sik is better than the dentist?

Of course Du-sik is a great guy, but Dr. Yoon isn't too bad either.

You can't vote for both people. Is it Hye-jin or Chief Hong?

홍반장. 혹시 나 좋아해?

짜증 나, 진짜.
대체 무슨 뇌 내 망상을 거치면 커피 마시자는 말이
좋아한다는 말로 번역되냐? 뭐 도끼병이야?

아니, 혹시나 해서. 나름 합리적인 의심이거든?
그렇잖아. 신발도 찾아주고, 치과에 도와주러 온 것도 그렇고.

Chief Hong. Do you like me or something?

That's ridiculous.

How delusional do you have to be for your brain

to translate an invitation to a cup of coffee to "I like you"? Are you a narcissist?

No, I just- It's a reasonable suspicion.

Think about it. You found my shoe for me and helped me back at the clinic.

홍반장이랑 나랑은 소셜 포지션이 다르잖아.
사람은 비슷한 환경일수록 잘 맞는다는 말 들어봤지?
가치관이랑 라이프스타일도 비슷하고 아무래도 부딪히는 일이 적을 테니까.
내가 홍반장을 평가하려는 게 아니라, 그냥 확실히 해두자는 의미에서...

나도 나지만, 참 너도 너다.
쉽게 좀 살자. 그렇게 살면 안 피곤하냐?

You and I have different social positions.
Have you heard that people with similar backgrounds tend to get along better?
It's because when two people have similar values and lifestyles, there will be less conflict.
I'm not trying to judge you. I'm just wanted to clear up...

I know I'm weird in my own ways, but you're so...
Don't be so calculating. Isn't it tiring to live like that?

사람들은 홍반장이 아깝다던데?

팔이 안으로 굽는다지만 진짜 너무하네.
나 의사야. 치대 나온 몸이라고!

홍반장은 서울대 나왔어.

People are saying that Chief Hong is too good for you.

I get that they're biased towards him because he's from here, but this is just too much.
I'm a doctor. I graduated from dentistry school.

Chief Hong is from Seoul National University.

미안. 남녀칠세부동석인데 내가 너무 가까이 걸었지?

뭐야, 갑자기?

내 섣부른 행동이 치과한테 오해를 제공할까 봐.
내가 자기를 좋아한다는.
세상이 참 각박해지기는 했나 봐.
사소한 친절마저 호감으로 확대 해석되는 거 보면.
나 오늘 절대 절대 치과 보고 싶어서 온 거 아니야.

Oops sorry. You're a conservative girl, but I walked too close, right?

What's this about all of a sudden?

I'm just making sure that my thoughtless actions won't cause any more
misunderstandings such as you thinking that I like you.
I guess the world has gotten colder
seeing as how my small act of kindness was mistaken for interest.
Oh and I just want to be clear. I didn't come here to see you.

밥 먹는데 뭘 차까지 타고 옆동네로 오냐?

공진에는 너무 아는 사람이 많단 말이야.
여기 아는 사람 없지?

Why did we have to drive to the next neighborhood just to eat?

There's too many nosy people in Gongjin.
You don't know anyone here, right?

세상에는 돈, 성공 말고도 많은 가치 있는 것들이 있어.
행복, 자기만족, 세계평화, 사랑...
여하튼, 인생은 수학공식이 아니라고!
미적분처럼 계산이 딱딱 나오지도 않을 뿐더러 정답도 없어.

There's other valuable things in life than just money and success.

Happiness, self-satisfaction, world peace, love...

In any case, life isn't some mathematical equation.

It can't be calculated like calculus and there's no right answer.

오늘 비 온다는 말은 없었던 것 같은데.

나 우산 있어.
비상시를 대비해서 우산을 갖고 다니거든.
...우산이 어디 갔지?

이거 찾아?
두고 갔더라. 그날.

It didn't say it would rain today.

I have an umbrella.
I always carry an umbrella with me in case it rains.
...Where did my umbrella go?

Are you looking for this?
You left it that day.

미쳤어? 다 젖었잖아!

어때? 좀 시원해진 것 같지 않아?

아니, 찝찝해. 꿉꿉하고.

그러면 어때. 그냥 그런대로 널 좀 놔둬.
소나기 없는 인생이 어디 있겠어!
이럴 때는 어차피 우산을 써도 젖어.
이럴 땐 에이 모르겠다 하고 그냥 확 맞아버리는 거야.
그냥 놀자. 나랑.

Are you crazy? I'm soaked!

What do you think? Feel refreshed?

No, I feel gross and damp.

So what, just accept it.
Life is full of unexpected events!
Even with an umbrella, you'd get wet.
At times like this, you should just say "whatever" and get soaked.
Come on, play with me.

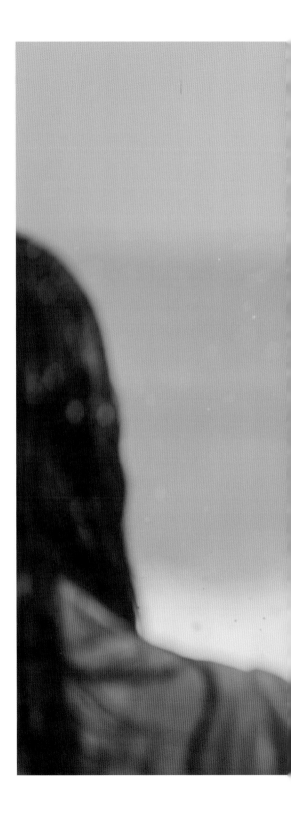

이깟 비 좀 맞는다고 큰일 안 나지?

모르지. 내일 또 아플 수도.

See? Getting wet from the rain isn't too bad, right?

Who knows. I might get sick tomorrow.

뜨겁다... 너무.

It's so... hot.

홍반장.
우리 그날 밤에 말이야.
진짜 아무 일도 없었어?

어. 없었는데.

Chief Hong.

About that night...

did nothing really happen?

Yeah, nothing happened.

6

당신의 시선이, 우정을 넘어선 순간
The moment you wanted to be more-than-friends

두식과의 키스가 떠오르자 혼란스러운 혜진. 어찌할지 모르겠는 혜진과 달리 두식은 너무나 태연하다. 심지어 생물학적 위기를 잘 넘겨야 진정한 친구가 될 수 있다는 속 뒤집히는 소리까지! 참다못한 혜진은 더는 얽히고 싶지 않으니 선을 지켜달라고 두식에게 선전포고 한다.

한편, 공진의 마을 축제 '등대가요제'를 앞두고 1등 상금을 쟁취하기 위해 마을 사람들 모두가 앞다투어 신청서를 제출한다. 그렇게 등대가요제 당일. 춘재, 남숙 등이 무대에 오르고, 이를 심드렁하게 바라보던 혜진 앞에 두식이 선다. 누가 좀 다쳤다는 말에 두식을 따라 무대 뒤편으로 가보니 춤 연습을 하다 다친 주리가 앉아 있다. 이대로는 안 된다며 혜진이 만류하지만, 덧니 교정을 위해서는 1등 상금이 꼭 필요하다며 주리 역시 만만치 않게 단호하다. 결심 끝에 혜진은 주리와 함께 무대에 오르고, 쪽팔림도 나누면 반이 된다며 두식도 합류하는데. 주리의 노래에 맞춰 춤을 추는 두 사람! 냉전 중이던 둘은 그렇게 다시 은근슬쩍 가까워진다.

등대가요제가 끝나고 바다 위로 피어오르는 폭죽을 함께 바라보는 혜진과 두식. 그 순간 누군가 툭 쳐 무게중심을 잃은 두식이 바다에 빠질 뻔하고, 바로 이어 그를 안아 지탱하는 사람, 성현이다! 혜진의 첫사랑 성현 선배.

After suddenly remembering her kiss with Du-sik, Hye-jin is very flustered. Unlike Hye-jin, Du-sik appears very calm and acts as if nothing has happened. He even says that overcoming this sort of "biological crisis" is a necessary step to becoming good friends. Annoyed by this, Hye-jin says that she does not want to get involved with him anymore and warns him not to cross the line.

Meanwhile, the townspeople are scrambling to submit their applications for the Lighthouse Song Festival after hearing about the first place prize. On the day of the festival, Du-sik asks for Hye-jin because someone had gotten hurt. It turns out that Chun-jae's daughter, Ju-ri, hurt her ankle while practicing her dance backstage. Hye-jin tells Ju-ri that she shouldn't perform, but Ju-ri is determined to perform and win the first place prize so she can pay for her braces. Hye-jin gives in and decides to support Ju-ri on the stage. Du-sik quickly joins in, saying that he will share the embarrassment with her. Hye-jin and Du-sik dance to Ju-ri's song and the cold air between them starts to melt.

After the festival ends, Hye-jin and Du-sik watch the fireworks above the ocean together. Du-sik gets pushed by someone that is passing by and loses his balance. Right as he is about to fall into the ocean, someone catches him. This someone is no one other than Hye-jin's first love: Seong-hyeon!

아무리 술김이라지만 천하의 윤혜진이 먼저 키스를 했다고?
홍반장은 뭐래?

분명 기억하는 것 같은데, 모르는 척하더라.

그거네. 그거 때문에 윤혜진 기분이 이렇게 다운돼 있었네.
너 홍반장에 대해서 어떻게 생각해?
네가 누구 때문에 이렇게까지 동요하는 거 오랜만이잖아.

I know you were drunk, but I can't believe you of all people initiated a kiss.
What did Chief Hong say?

I'm sure he remembers, but he's playing dumb.

That's it! That's why you're feeling so down.
What do you think about Chief Hong?
It's been a while since you've been so troubled over a guy like this.

2주 뒤에 등대가요제 있는 거 다들 아시죠?

Everyone's aware that we have the Lighthouse Song Festival coming up in two weeks, right?

홍반장 한번 나가봐. 노래 잘하잖아.

그래, 윤선생님이랑 둘이 나가면 되겠네. 듀엣으로다가.

Chief Hong, you should do it. You're good at singing.

She's right, you can enter with Dr. Yoon as a duet.

둘이 멀찌감치 떨어져 앉은 거 보면 몰라?
둘 사이가 진짜 끝났다는 거잖아.

끝나긴 뭘 끝나요. 아예 시작을 안 했는데.
저랑 홍반장 아무 사이도 아니에요.
자꾸 이렇게 말도 안 되는 루머 유포하시면 저 가만 안 있어요.

Can't you tell from how far apart they're sitting?

Their relationship is already over.

What's there to end? It never started to begin with.

There's nothing between Chief Hong and me.

If you keep spreading these ridiculous rumors, I won't stand still.

우리 둥글둥글하게 좀 살자. 친구로서 충고하는 거야.

요새 나랑 좀 엮였다고 진짜 나랑 뭐라도 되는 줄 아나 본데,
나 아무하고나 친구 안 해.

아무나?

이렇게 된 거 다 얘기할게. 나 홍반장 좀 피곤해.
자꾸 소문나는 것도 싫고 더는 얽히고 싶지 않아.

나 너 좀 변한 줄 알았는데... 내가 착각했네.

Be more easygoing. That's my advice as a friend.

I think you're getting the wrong idea because I've been involved with you lately,
but I don't make friends with just anyone.

Anyone?

While we're on this topic, I'll just say it. I get tired around you.
I don't like being the center of all these rumors, and I don't want to get involved with you anymore.

You know, I thought you had changed a little... but it seems like I was mistaken.

가요제 지원서 내러 온 거 아니지?
어머야라 진짜네, 이 오빠.

너는 왜 아무 데나 다 있니, 남숙아?

Don't tell me you're here to apply for
the singing contest.
Oh my gosh, I was right.

Why are you everywhere Nam-suk?

치과, 나랑 잠깐 어디 좀 가.
급해. 얼른.

왜 또 이래.

누가 좀 다쳤어.

Ms. Dentist, come with me for a second.
It's urgent. Hurry.

Why are you calling me?

Someone got hurt.

1등 하자. 언니 2등 싫어해.
홍반장, 이 춤 알아?

아니, 몰라.

근데 왜 올라왔어, 빨리 내려가.

쪽팔림도 나누면 반이 될까 싶어서.
그리고 이런 무대는 어차피 실력보단 흥으로 승부하는 거야!

Let's win first place. I don't like being second.

Chief Hong, do you know this dance?

No, I don't.

Then why did you come up? Go back down.

I thought we could share the embarrassment.

Besides, for these kinds of things, it's more about getting people excited than being skilled.

무슨 일 있어야 전화하나, 그냥 했어요.
아빠가 그때 주신 화분. 꽃이 폈어요.

Do I have to have a reason to call? I just wanted to.
The plant you gave me bloomed recently.

그래? 행운목은 꽃이 7년에 한 번 핀다던데.
그 꽃을 본 사람에게는 인생에 다시없을 행운이 온다더라.

Really? I heard that those plants only bloom once every seven years.
It's said that the person who sees it bloom will be granted the greatest luck of their life.

나 요새 솔직히 치과 다시 재수 없어지려 그랬거든?
근데 오늘은 좀 멋있고... 기특했다.

To be honest, recently I was starting to hate you again.

But today, you were really cool... I'm proud of you.

누가 낭만에 불을 붙였네.
쓸데없이, 이쁘게.

It looks like someone got the romance going.
How unnecessarily pretty.

7

당신의 외로움이, 나에게 기대온 순간
The moment you leaned on me

시청률 보증수표 지성현 피디의 방문에 들썩이는 공진. 게다가 공진에서 새 예능 프로그램 〈갯마을 베짱이〉를 촬영한다고 하니 더욱 설레는 마을 사람들이다. 특별했던 삼자대면 후, 세 사람은 함께 술자리를 하게 되고, 죽이 잘 맞아 재잘재잘 떠드는 혜진과 성현을 보며 두식은 묘한 소외감을 느낀다. 성현은 이 자리에서 두식에게 프로그램 현장 가이드를 맡아줄 것을 부탁하고, 두식이 거절하자 성현은 게임으로 결정하자고 제안한다. 하지만 승부가 나지 않아 게임이 계속되고, 결국 완전히 취해버린 세 사람! 그대로 두식의 집에서 함께 잠이 든다.

〈갯마을 베짱이〉 촬영 장소로 감리의 집을 찜한 성현! 하지만 감리는 단번에 거절한다. 포기를 모르는 성현은 친절을 베풀고 선물 공세를 하며 천천히 감리에게 다가간다.

한편, 두식과 함께 감리의 집에서 이불 빨래를 하게 된 혜진. 두식과 마주 보고 이불을 밟다가 이마가 '쿵' 하자 지난밤의 기억이 스친다. 두식이 자신의 어깨에 얼굴을 묻던 장면. 그렇게 혼란스러워진 혜진 앞에 나타난 성현과 DOS의 멤버 준! 모두 함께 감리의 집에서 저녁을 먹게 되고 시끌벅적한 이날 밤이 참으로 좋았던 감리는 결국 촬영을 허락하고 만다.

Gongjin becomes more lively upon the arrival of Producer Ji Seong-hyeon, who is known for his guarantee of high viewer ratings. The townspeople become more excited after hearing that he will be filming a new program called *The Seashore Grasshopper* in Gongjin. After the unexpected three-way meeting, Hye-jin, Du-sik, and Seong-hyeon go out drinking together. Du-sik feels like an outsider watching Hye-jin and Seong-hyeon having fun catching up. While drinking, Seong-hyeon asks Du-sik to be an on-site guide for the program. Du-sik refuses. Seong-hyeon suggests it be decided with a game, but they are too drunk to finish the game. The three of them fall asleep in Du-sik's house.

Seong-hyeon decides he wants to film *The Seashore Grasshopper* at Ms. Gam-ri's house. Ms. Gam-ri is strongly against it and does not give her permission. Seong-hyeon, who doesn't know how to give up, gradually gets closer to Ms. Gam-ri by being friendly and giving her gifts.

Du-sik and Hye-jin somehow end up washing blankets at Ms. Gam-ri's house. As Hye-jin is stepping on the blankets with Du-sik, she accidentally bumps her forehead on Du-sik. Just then, she recalls a memory from last night: Du-sik burying his face in her shoulder. Seong-hyeon and June, a member of the hot boy group DOS, stop by Ms. Gam-ri's house. All five of them end up having dinner together at Ms. Gam-ri's house. Ms. Gam-ri enjoys the lively atmosphere from having people over and gives permission for filming at her house.

한참을 찾아다녔는데 이제야 만나네.

성현... 선배?

I've been looking for you for a while.
I finally found you.

Seong-hyeon... sunbae*?

* sunbae: In Korean, sunbae means an upperclassman
  or senior.

시청률 보증수표! 지성현 피디님!

제가 이번에 공진에서 〈갯마을 베짱이〉라고 새 예능 프로그램을 찍게 됐습니다.

He guarantees high viewer ratings! He's producer Ji Seong-hyeon!

I'm planning to shoot a new variety show called *The Seashore Grasshopper* here in Gongjin.

치과. 저 양반이랑은 어떻게 알아?

대학 선배야.

Ms. Dentist, how do you know that man?

He's my upperclassman from college.

치과 데려다주고 우리끼리 한잔 어때? 콜?

뭐야? 갑자기.
왜 나 빼놓고 둘이 술을 마셔?

치과는 내일 일찍 출근하셔야 된다며.

아니, 12시까지는 괜찮아.
아, 여기 홍반장 집이네.

How about we drink together after
dropping Ms. Dentist home? Sound good?

What's this all of a sudden?
Why would you two go for a drink
without me?

You said you have to go to work early
tomorrow.

No, it's alright. I can stay out until 12.
Oh look, it's Chief Hong's house.

선배를 나만 빼고 여기로 데려오려던 저의가 뭐야?
혹시 내 얘기 하려고?

Why did you want to bring him here without me?
Were you going to talk about me behind my back?

선배한테 쓸데없는 얘기하지 마!
특히 우리 그날 밤 일.

아아, 우리 그 생물학적 위기?

뭐 해?

Don't say any unnecessary things to him!
Especially about what happened that night.

Oh~ You mean our biological crisis?

What are you guys doing?

우리 프로그램 현장 가이드 좀 맡아줘.

내가 이기면 그쪽이 가이드 맡아주는 거고, 그쪽이 이기면 거절해도 돼.

Please be a guide for my program.

If I win this game, you'll become our guide. If you win, I'll give up.

왜 이렇게 무거워...
밖에서 자면 입 돌아간다니까...
홍반장... 내가 너 생명의 은인이야.

Why are you so heavy...
You can't sleep outside like this or
you'll freeze to death.
Chief Hong... I just saved your life.

저기 혜진아, 번호 좀 줄래?
어제 이것도 못 물어봤네.

Oh Hye-jin, can I have your number?
I forgot to ask yesterday.

치과는?

어, 갔어. 나도 가볼게.

저기, 라면 먹고 갈래?

Where's Ms. Dentist?

Oh, she just left. I'll get going too.

Hey, Do you want to eat ramyeon?

저, 어르신. 비워달라는 게 아니라
빌려주십사 부탁드리는 거예요.

그만 가오! 아무리 떼를 써봐야 소용엄싸.

Ma'am, we're not asking you to move out,
we're just asking if we could borrow
the house.

Go already! There ain't no use
no matter how much ya try.

할머니!
치과가 이불 빨래 도와주고 간대!
뭐 해? 옷 안 갈아입고?

Grandma!
Ms. Dentist said she'll help wash the sheets before leaving!
What are you waiting for? Hurry up and go change.

뭐 하냐?

갑자기 무슨 이상한 장면이 떠올라서.

What are you doing?

I just remembered a weird situation.

지금 이 상황이 더 이상한 장면이라고 생각은 안 하고?

Don't you think that this situation is way weirder?

고생들 많았싸.
우선 이걸로 요기부터 하고 있으라니.

Good work ya two.
Here, eat a little snack first.

아는 동생이랑 밥 먹으러 가다가 잠깐 들른 거예요.
잠깐 인사라도 하고 가라고 할까요?
준아, 들어와!

I was just on my way to grab dinner with a friend.
Should I call him here to say hi?
June, come in!

니 오늘 그 피디 장제이 좀 데꼬 오라니.
집 비워준다 해.
사람들이 시끌시끌 놀더 가믄 이 집도 덜 외롭지 않겠나?

할머니 어제는 안 외로웠구나?

I need ya to bring that producer fellow to me today.

Let'im know that he can borrow ma house.

Wouldn't this house feel less lonely if there's more people?

Grandma, I guess you didn't feel lonely yesterday.

두식이, 홍반장.
여기서 머 해? 자는 고야?

Du-sik, Chief Hong.
What are you doing here? You sleeping?

가지 마...
나만 두고 가지 마...
가지 마...

안 가.
아무 데도 안 가.
걱정하지 마, 홍반장.

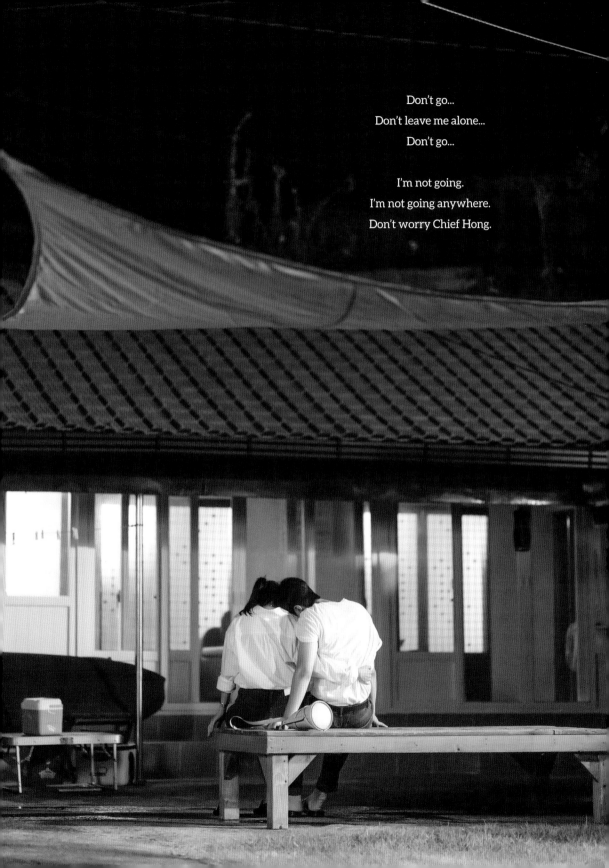

Don't go...
Don't leave me alone...
Don't go...

I'm not going.
I'm not going anywhere.
Don't worry Chief Hong.

8

당신의 존재가, 어둠을 지우는 순간
The moment your existence erases the darkness

성현은 두식에게 혜진이 만나는 사람이 있는지를 묻고, 성현의 마음을 눈치챈 두식은 마음이 심란해지는 한편 자꾸만 질투가 난다. 하지만 정작 혜진은 치과 일로 골치가 아프다. 환자들이 자꾸만 치료를 중단하기 때문! 이유를 추적하던 혜진은 그 배후에 남숙이 있음을 알게 되는데, 오히려 적반하장으로 나오는 남숙! 이로 인해 둘 사이는 완전히 틀어져버린다.

한편, 공진에 납치 미수 사건이 발생하며 모두가 불안에 떤다. 성현은 혜진을 찾아가 행운의 라마 인형과 호신용품을 선물하고, 마침 혜진의 집 주변을 순찰하던 두식은 이 둘과 마주친다. 당황한 두식은 우산을 빌려준다는 혜진의 말을 쳐내고 비를 맞으며 황급히 자리를 뜬다.

다음 날, 남숙이 보이스피싱범과 함께 있는 현장을 지나치게 된 혜진! 맞은편에서 걸어오던 두식과 합세해 범인 검거에 성공하고, 이를 계기로 혜진과 남숙은 서로에 대한 앙금을 풀어버린다. 두식은 전날 맞은 비로 심한 몸살에 걸린 데다 보이스피싱범을 잡는 과정에서 넘어지며 찰과상을 입는다. 집에서 혼자 끙끙 앓는 두식을 찾아와 함께해주는 혜진. 약을 발라주고, 먹고 싶은 음식을 물어봐주고, 죽을 끓여준다.

드디어 시작된 〈갯마을 베짱이〉 촬영! 공진 사람들 다 모인 촬영장에 혜진이 보이지 않자 궁금해진 두식이고, 혜진은 늦은 밤 누군가 자신을 쫓아오는 소리에 잔뜩 긴장했다가 앞에 선 두식을 보고 덥석 안기는데...

Seong-hyeon asks Du-sik if Hye-jin is seeing anyone. Du-sik realizes that Seong-hyeon has feelings for Hye-jin and starts to feel upset and jealous. Meanwhile, Hye-jin is facing difficulties at her workplace. For some unknown reason, her clients keep quitting their treatment mid-way! Hye-jin later realizes that Nam-suk is the cause, as she was referring everyone to a cheaper technician. The two are now on bad terms.

In the town, people are feeling anxious because there have been many attempted kidnappings recently. Seong-hyeon gives Hye-jin a lucky llama charm and some self-defense tools. Du-sik, who has been patrolling around Hye-jin's house, encounters the two. Feeling flustered, he leaves hurriedly in the rain despite Hye-jin's offer to lend him an umbrella.

The next day, Hye-jin witnesses Nam-suk getting scammed by a voice phisher. With the help of Du-sik, who was coincidentally on the other side of the street, Hye-jin succeeds in getting the criminal arrested. Through this experience, Hye-jin and Nam-suk clear their misunderstandings towards each other. Du-sik goes home injured and sick from catching the criminal and getting soaked in the rain the day before. Hye-jin visits Du-sik's house to take care of him. She treats his wounds, asks him what he wants to eat, and cooks him porridge.

Finally, the shooting of *The Seashore Grasshopper* begins! All of the townspeople gather at the set to watch the filming. Du-sik can't find Hye-jin in the crowd and gets curious where she is. Later at night, Hye-jin feels paranoid that someone is following her. Just then, she sees Du-sik in front of her and runs to hug him.

혜진이 만나는 사람 있어?

Is Hye-jin seeing anyone?

...아니? 없는 거 같던데.

근데 그걸 왜 나한테 물어봐?

본인이 직접 물어보면 되지, 왜 귀찮고 입 아프게 그걸 나한테.

...No. I don't think so.

But why are you asking me that?

You can just ask her directly. Why are you bothering me about this?

서핑이라는 게 인생이랑 비슷해.
좋은 파도가 오면은 올라타고 또 잘 내려가고.
파도가 너무 높거나 없는 날에는 겸허히 받아들이고.

Surfing is very similar to life.
If a good wave comes, you can ride up and down the wave with ease.
On days when the waves are too high or too low, you should just accept it as it is.

이거 피디 양반이 서울서 사온 빵들인데...
이름이 뭐더라?

That young producer fellow bought us bread from Seoul...
What were they called again?

아주 지피디 바쁘네. 동에 번쩍 서에 번쩍 난리가 났네.
자기가 무슨 홍길동이야? 홍씨는 나거든?

Producer Ji sure is busy, stirring up things in the west and east and showing up all over town.
What is he, Hong Gildong*? I'm the only Hong of this town.

* Hong Gildong: In a Korean novel, *The Biography of Hong Gildong*, Hong Gildong is a hero-character that goes
  around the country resolving problems and punishing criminals.

목 디스크 있어서, 보호대.

괜한 얘기를 들어가지고... 신경 쓰이게.

The neck brace is because of my herniated disk.

Listening to this useless talk just gave me more to worry about.

납치 미수라니,
혼자 사는 여자들은 좀 무섭겠어요.

To think there was an attempted kidnapping.
Women who live alone must be terrified.

페루에 간 적이 있거든?
거기서는 라마 미라를 집 처마에 달면은 행운이 온다고 믿는대.
당분간 빌려줄게, 내 행운.

I went to Peru before.
People there believe that putting a mummified llama on your roof will bring good luck.
I'll lend you my luck for a while.

오늘 비 온다는 말 없었던 것 같은데.
형 먼저 들어가세요.

됐어. 이깟 비 좀 맞는다고 어떻게 안 돼.

I don't think there was rain in today's forecast.
Hyung, you should go home.

It's fine. A little rain won't hurt me.

불이 아직도 약하네?
시청에 민원 넣은 지가 언젠데!

The light is still broken?
It's been forever since I filed a request
at the city hall!

깜깜해졌는데,
치과는 아직도 안 들어온 건가?

It's gotten dark,

but Ms. Dentist isn't home yet?

선배. 이따가 이거 쓰고 가요.
나도 빌려줄게요.

좋아. 서로 하나씩 빌려줬네.

Sunbae, you should take this umbrella with you.
I'll lend it to you too.

Alright, now we're both lending each other something.

나 순찰 도는 중.

치과, 마침 잘 만났다.

이거 오가피인데

집에 너무 많아서 그냥 두면 썩을까 봐.

너 먹어.

I'm on patrol.

Ms. Dentist, I'm glad I ran into you.

I have too much Acanthopanax at home.

I was worried they'd rot before I get to eat all of them, so I brought you some.

Here, take it.

홍반장, 안색이 너무 안 좋은 거 아니야?

어제 비 맞아서 그런 거 아니야?

나를 뭘로 보고! 그깟 비 좀 맞는다고 사람 안 죽어.

Chief Hong, you don't look so well.

Isn't it because you got rained on yesterday?

What do you take me for? People won't die just because of a little rain.

잠깐만요.
왜 여기서 현금 거래를 해요?
보이스피싱이죠?

Wait a minute.

Why are you giving him cash?

This is a voice phishing scam, right?

너 뭐 잘못했어? 절도? 사기?

알지도 못하면서 나를 왜 잡아?

치과가 잡으라길래.

What did you do anyway? Theft? Fraud?

Why did you come after me if you don't even know?

Because Ms. Dentist told me to.

이리 내.
따가워도 좀 참아.

Give me your arm.
This might sting a bit.

홍반장 얼굴이 더 빨개졌어.

아... 열...
열이 있어서 그래.

Chief Hong, your face is redder than before.

Oh... my fever...
It's just because I have a fever.

밥은 먹었어? 뭐 먹고 싶은 거 있어?

귤?
그냥 입맛도 없고 상큼한 게 순간 생각나서.

빈속에 산 많은 거 먹으면 위 다 긁혀.
아플 땐 죽을 먹어야지.

Did you eat yet? Is there anything you want to eat?

Tangerines?
I don't have an appetite, so I just thought of something citrusy.

Eating sour foods is bad for an empty stomach.
When you're sick, you should just have porridge.

아플 때 혼자 있으면 서러워.
남들 다 아는 걸 왜 홍반장은 몰라?

It's sad to be alone when you're sick.
That's common knowledge, how come you don't know that?

혹시 뭐 깨지는 소리나 비명 소리 같은 거 들려도
절대 부엌에는 얼씬도 하지 마. 알았지?

Even if you hear something like plates breaking or screaming,
don't go anywhere near the kitchen, okay?

진짜 잠들었네.
웬일로 말을 잘 듣는대?

He actually fell asleep.

It's unlike him to be so obedient.

하, 이거 봐? 어떻게 이런 맛이 나지?
정말 완벽하게 맛대가리가 없네! 와...
쌀이랑 물로 뭘 이렇게 망치기도 쉽지 않은데...
이래놓고 남기지 말라고?

God, how can porridge taste like this?
It's couldn't possibly taste any worse. Wow...
It's not easy to ruin rice and water...
And she wants me to finish all of this?

언제 놓고 간 거야?

When did she leave these here?

뭐야. 불이 나갔네?

Huh, the light went out.

치과?
영업시간 끝난 지가 언젠데!
제발 일찍 일찍 좀...

Ms. Dentist?
It's been hours since your clinic closed!
You shouldn't be out so late...

갯마을
차차차